S0-BEG-214

B C MAMBO

By Erik Craddock

Very special thanks to Eric Demski, whose hard work, friendship, guidance, and dedication helped make this book possible.

This is a work of fiction. Names, characters, places, and incidents either are the product of the author's imagination or are used fictitiously. Any resemblance to actual persons, living or dead, events, or locales is entirely coincidental.

Copyright © 2009 by Erik Craddock

All rights reserved.

Published in the United States by Random House Children's Books, a division of Random House, Inc., New York.
Random House and colophon are registered trademarks of Random House, Inc.

Visit us on the Web! www.randomhouse.com/kids

Educators and librarians, for a variety of teaching tools, visit us at www.randomhouse.com/teachers

www.stonerabbit.com

Library of Congress Cataloging-in-Publication Data
Craddock, Erik.
BC mambo / by Erik Craddock. — 1st ed.
p. cm. — (Stone Rabbit ; bk. 1)
Summary: After Stone Rabbit is transported back to prehistoric times, his bottle of barbecue
sauce becomes the key ingredient in a power-hungry Neanderthal's plan to dominate the world.
ISBN 978-0-375-84360-0 (trade) — ISBN 978-0-375-93922-8 (lib. bdg.)
1. Graphic novels. [1. Graphic novels. 2. Rabbits—Fiction. 3. Prehistoric peoples—Fiction.
4. Time travel—Fiction. 5. Humorous stories.] I. Title.
PZ7.7.C73Baak 2009
[Fic]—dc22   2008000681

MANUFACTURED IN MALAYSIA
10 9 8 7 6 5 4 3 2 1
First Edition

Random House Children's Books supports the First Amendment and celebrates the right to read.

8

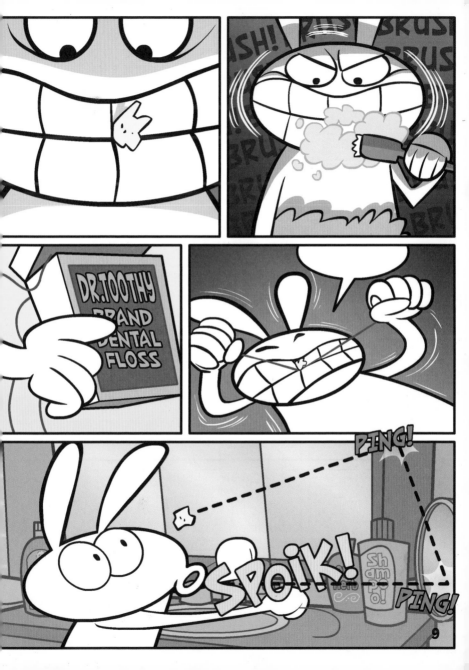

9

15

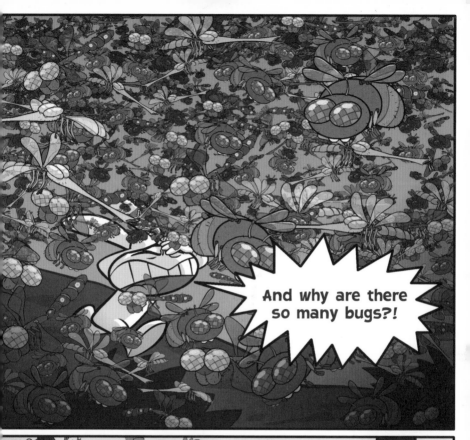

17

23

25

CHILDREN'S ROOM

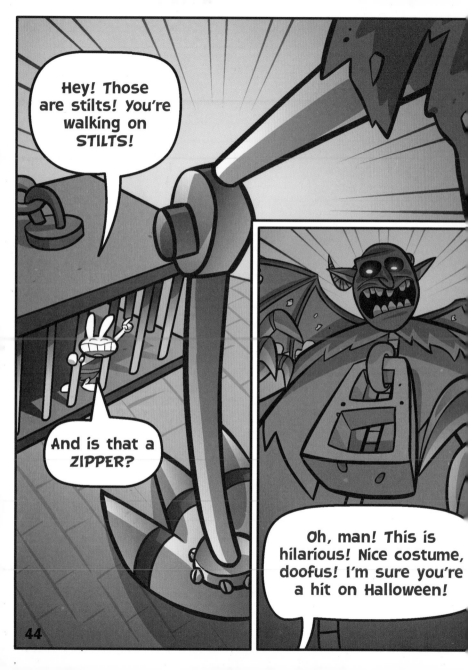

46

49

51

55

57

Hey, big guy! Stop digging for gold and use your boomerang to hit the cage release!

71

81

85

91

94

95

CHILDREN'S BOOK

Woodson

J 741.5 C 2009
Craddock, Erik.
BC mambo

6-22-11

GARY PUBLIC LIBRARY

3 9222 03028 936 2